For Laura and Michael: May you always find shelter from the storm,
and may the sun shine brightly in your lives.
With love,
Rachel

An Umbrella for Alex

Rachel Rashkin-Shoot, MS, Psy.D

D1616450

Personality Disorder Awareness Network
A not-for-profit corporation
PO Box 79468 • Atlanta, GA 30357
Tel: 1-601-PD-AWARE (1-601-732-9273)
www.PDAN.org
Published by PDAN PRESS

Foreword

Since the first edition of An Umbrella for Alex was published six years ago, more than a thousand families have benefited from the insightful story and useful advice in this wise children's book. Meanwhile, unbridled emotions continued raining on children and families. Demand for umbrellas to protect children's emotions kept on growing. We reprinted An Umbrella for Alex, again and again.

We read the reviews, and listen to your feedback. This year, we felt it was time to introduce this new and updated color version of this very nice children's book.

Designer Danni Diol did a fantastic job bringing to life the world of Alex in colors. Author Rachel Rashkin-Shoot made a few text improvements. It is still the wonderful story of little Alex and his family; a story that aims to transcend gender, providing boys and girls, mothers and fathers, with words of hope. His parents are at times in a stormy or cloudy mood, yet they love Alex deeply. Despite the challenges he faces, Alex values himself, continues to develop in healthy ways, and learns great skills that help him achieve his full potential.

Thank you for your support throughout the years! We look forward to hearing from you. It is through your efforts and kind interactions that we are able to improve the world.

Frederic V. Bien, Ph.D
President, 2012

**personality disorder
awareness network**

Did you ever wonder what a mood is?
A mood describes the way you feel.
Everyone has moods, kids and grown-ups too.
They are a normal part of being a person.
There are lots of different kinds of moods. Some
are: happy, sad, grumpy, excited, or angry.

You might be in an excited or happy mood
if you get invited to a birthday party, or win
a contest! When I feel excited, I run around
and do a silly dance, and my stomach feels all
fluttery inside.

You might be in a grumpy mood if it's raining
outside, especially if you wanted to ride your
bike or play at the park.

When I feel grumpy, I wear a frown on my
face and say things like: "hmph" and "grrrr!"
You might be in a sad mood if you find out that
your good friend is moving far away,
or if you lose something special. Sometimes
when I'm sad, I look out the window and watch
the clouds roll by, or feel the warm
sun on my face.

What kind of mood are you in right now?

Nobody stays in the same mood all the time. But when people stay in the same mood most of the time, that's called having an even mood. My Dad has an even mood and I like that.

When he comes home from work, he greets me with a big hug and says-"Hi there, Alex! How was your day at school today?"

Of course Dad gets angry, sad and grumpy just like all people do. But mostly he's a pretty happy guy and feels like the same Dad every day. I feel safe around him because I know what he will act like when I see him.

Not everybody has an even mood. There is a special part of our brain that controls feelings. When it isn't working, people might have unpredictable (un-pre-dict-able) moods.

That's a pretty big word. Unpredictable means that we don't know ahead of time what something is going to be like. Kind of like the weather!

Just when it looks dark and rainy, the sun might come out! When people have unpredictable moods, they aren't sure which mood will "come out" next. They might feel happy one minute and mad the next! When you live in a house with someone who has a problem with moods, it can feel confusing and scary.

Do you have a mom or dad with
unpredictable moods?

My Mom has unpredictable moods. She has a hard time controlling what mood she will be in each day. It means I don't know what she will act like when I wake up in the morning or when I come home from school. That can be really confusing!

Remember how unpredictable moods can be like the weather? Well, just like the wind can blow in one direction and then quickly change in another, so can Mom's mood. She can feel okay one minute, but very angry the next. It can be really hard to keep track of all her moods.

Sometimes, her mood will get bigger and bigger and BIGGER. It's like she put an ugly mask on her face and turned into someone else. She yells and says mean things that hurt my feelings (and my ears!)!

She might shout-"Alex, you are bothering me!! Get out of this room right now!!" When Mom yells like that, she doesn't feel like a mom at all! I get so mad that I even wish I had a different mother!!

Once I yelled back and said-"I hate you! You are the worst mom in the whole world!" I ran to my room and slammed the door. I cried a lot and then felt better. When her words hurt me, I get so angry.

What do you do when you feel really angry?

Dad reminds me that it's okay and normal to feel mad. Even really, REALLY mad. It doesn't mean I'm bad or sick. And it doesn't mean I have the same problem that Mom does. He calls Mom's angry moods, "stormy" and he reminds me that Mom made her stormy mood all by herself.

It belongs to her and not us. We didn't cause it and we can't make it go away.

When Mom is having a hard time controlling her moods, we know how to protect ourselves.

I like to pretend Dad is a big umbrella
and he shelters me from "the storm."
Sometimes, we go out for a hamburger
with pickles. My favorite!

What do you do by yourself
when your mom or dad is in a
stormy or cloudy mood?

Mom has very sad moods, too. Dad calls those moods, "cloudy." Just like the sun hides behind the clouds, Mom needs to have time to hide from other people.

It helps her calm down and feel better. When cloudy moods come, Mom stays in her bed and I might not see her all day.

That scares me. I worry about how she is feeling, and I worry that I did something wrong that made her feel sad. I wonder if she'll ever come out of her room or if she'll stay there forever!

Sometimes when Mom is in a cloudy mood, she has visitors come over. They help her talk about why she's feeling so sad. Other times, I give her a hug and tell her I love her.

But even when Mom is having a rough time, Dad reminds me that she'll feel better soon and that I can still do fun things while she is recovering.

In fact, Mom and Dad wrote a note that I keep
by my bed. It says-"Alex is a terrific boy who
can have fun even when mom is in a stormy or
cloudy mood." I like to look at the note when
I'm feeling worried or afraid that Mom might
stay in a sad or angry mood forever.

What fun things do you do when your mom or dad is in a stormy or cloudy mood?

Dad isn't always home when Mom has a stormy or cloudy mood. When that happens, the best thing I can do is be my own umbrella and protect myself.

I can find something to do in my room or ride my bike around the block with my friend Sam. I make sure to do my homework and go to bed on time.

My friend, Sophie, down the block, has a Dad with unpredictable moods and sometimes we see each other at the playground and talk about things.

When Mom is feeling good, she can be a lot of fun! We go places together like the library or the zoo.

I like the funny voices she uses when she tells stories, and she always remembers how to make peanut butter sandwiches just the way I like them (with the chunky kind). Mom is also super at math and helps me with my homework.

When your mom or dad is feeling better, what special things do you like to do together?

It's important to find someone who you can talk to about what it feels like to have a mom or dad with unpredictable moods.

That person might be an adult, a good friend, or a therapist. A therapist's job is to help kids and grown ups understand all their feelings.

I talk to two people about what it's like for me to live in my house. My Dad and my therapist, Dr. Gillman.

My Dad takes me to Dr. Gillman's office every Wednesday after school. Sometimes we just talk and other times we draw or play games.

Seeing a therapist helps me understand all my confusing feelings, and that feels good. Talking to Dad helps, too. He reminds me that I didn't do anything wrong to make Mom's moods happen and I can't fix them.

And I don't have to worry that I can "catch" unpredictable moods in the same way I can catch a cold or cough.

It takes a lot of practice to be my own umbrella and to protect myself when Mom's moods are stormy or cloudy. But I'm getting better at it. And you can, too.

Who do you talk to about what it feels like to live in your house?

17

About the Author:

Rachel Rashkin-Shoot is a Clinical Psychologist in private practice, whose interests include parent-child relationships, early adolescent transitions and identity development throughout the lifespan.

She is the author of "*Feeling Better*": *A Kid's Book about Psychotherapy* (Magination Press, 2005). Rachel lives in Jerusalem, Israel with her husband and two children, and continues to write self-help books for children of all ages.

Notes on the 1st edition (2006)

It is estimated that about two percent of the general US population (six million people) meet the diagnostic criteria for Borderline Personality Disorder (BPD). Millions more may have enough BPD characteristics to cause significant problems in everyday living.

Many of those who suffer with this mental illness are parents. A parent with BPD may present with extreme mood swings, angry outbursts, and other volatile behaviors. This creates a confusing and chaotic family environment which may cause significant emotional and psychological distress for children with a BPD parent. An Umbrella for Alex is a reassuring and practical resource which tells the story of how a young boy copes with his mother's illness. It is the first book of its kind to directly address the experience of a child who shares a home with a BPD parent.

This book is published by the Personality Disorder Awareness Network, a non-profit group dedicated to increasing public awareness about personality disorders and their impact on children, relationships, and society at large.

For more information visit our website, www.PDAN.org.

Mary F. Gay, Ph.D, LPC
Past President

Updates for the 2nd edition (2012)

Recent research published by the National Institutes of Health (NIH) indicates that BPD afflicts up to 5.9% of adults or approximately 14 million Americans (Grant *et al.* 2008), and Narcissistic Personality Disorder (NPD) afflicts up to 6.2% of adults (Stinson *et al.* 2008). Some people fit both diagnoses, so experts estimate that nearly 10 percent of the US adult population has BPD and/or NPD (approx. 23 million Americans). Statistics in other countries are likely to be similar. BPD & NPD are important mental health issues all around the world.

ADDITIONAL RESOURCES FOR PARENTS

If you'd like to learn more about psychology and especially emotions management, we recommend these books and websites. You will also find additional books and websites on the subject. Please do exert caution with what you read and how you apply it. Managing emotions can be an art form.

Books

Stop Walking on Eggshells
Taking Your Life Back When Someone You Care About Has Borderline Personality Disorder
By Randi Kreger and Paul Mason, 2010

Also useful: **The Stop Walking on Eggshells Workbook**
Practical Strategies for Living with Someone Who Has Borderline Personality Disorder By Randi Kreger, 2008

Feeling Better: A Kid's Book About Therapy
Using a journal format, 12-year-old Maya chronicles her emotional ups and downs and describes the process of psychotherapy.
By Rachel Rashkin (Author) and Bonnie Adamson (Illustrator), 2005

Borderline Personality Disorder Demystified
An Essential Guide for Understanding and Living with BPD
By Robert Friedel, 2004

New Hope for People with Borderline Personality Disorder
Your Friendly, Authoritative Guide to the Latest in Traditional and Complementary Solutions
By Neil Bockian, 2002

Loving Someone with Borderline Personality Disorder
How to Keep Out-of-Control Emotions from Destroying Your Relationship
By Shari Manning, (Foreword by Marsha Linehan), 2011

Websites

Personality Disorder Awareness Network
www.pdan.org

Publisher of this book "An Umbrella for Alex". Offers ongoing support, education, commitment, and compassion for the individuals and families enduring the relational trauma caused by personality disorders. Through our informative books, child and adult-friendly website, and community of online professionals, we remain dedicated to the healing processes and empowerment of those who are either directly or indirectly affected by personality disorders.

Active Parenting
www.ActiveParenting.com

Publishers of award-winning, video-based parenting programs and material for individuals and professionals, since 1983.

BPD Central
www.BPDcentral.com

One of the longest-established and most popular websites about BPD. Offers great books and a large support community called "Welcome toOz".

Unhooked Books
www.UnhookedBooks.com

An online bookstore specialized in personality disorders and resolution of family conflicts. A great resource to find many more books, ebooks, and programs on this subject.

As the publisher of this book "An Umbrella for Alex," PDAN is a not-for-profit organization that works globally to increase awareness for personality disorders. We are here to offer ongoing support, education, commitment, and compassion for the individuals and families enduring the relational trauma caused by personality disorders. Through our informative books, child and adult-friendly website, and community of online professionals, we remain dedicated to the healing processes and empowerment of those who are either directly or indirectly affected by personality disorders.

personality disorder
awareness network

CPSIA information can be obtained at www.ICGtesting.com
Printed in the USA
LVOW010904280912

300693LV00004B/1/P